Move Over!

Waterbed SALE!

Story by Joy Cowley
Illustrations by Jean Pidgeon

The animals looked
in the door and said,
"The farmers brought home
a new water bed!"

3

The cow jumped on.
"Moo, moo!" she said.

"I want to sleep
on the water bed."

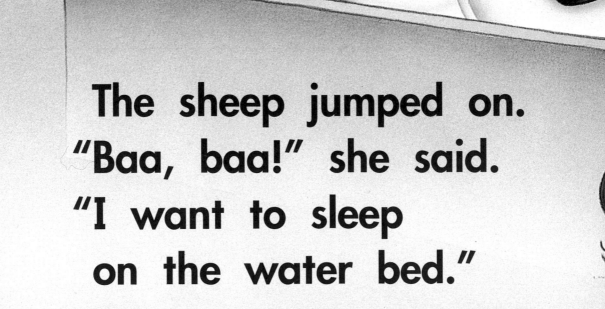

The sheep jumped on.
"Baa, baa!" she said.
"I want to sleep
on the water bed."

The pig jumped on.
"Oink, oink!" he said.
"I want to sleep
on the water bed."

The goat rushed in.
"Move over!" he said.
"I want my share
of the water bed."

"No room! No room!"
the animals said.
"You won't fit
on our water bed."

The goat got mad.
He butted his head
and stuck his horns
in the water bed.

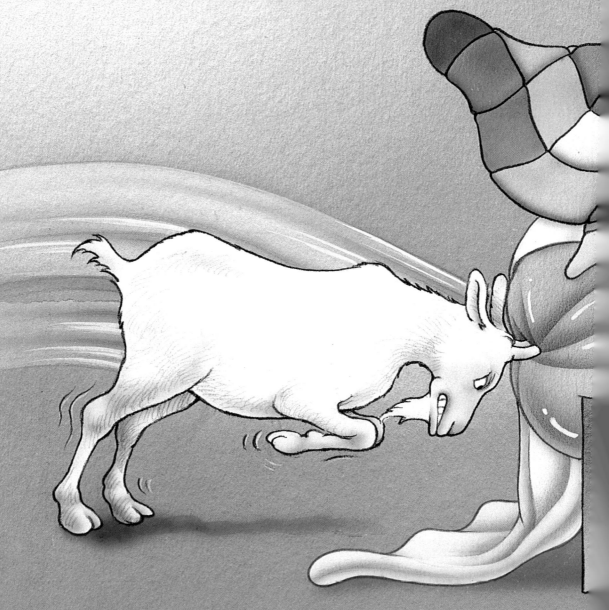

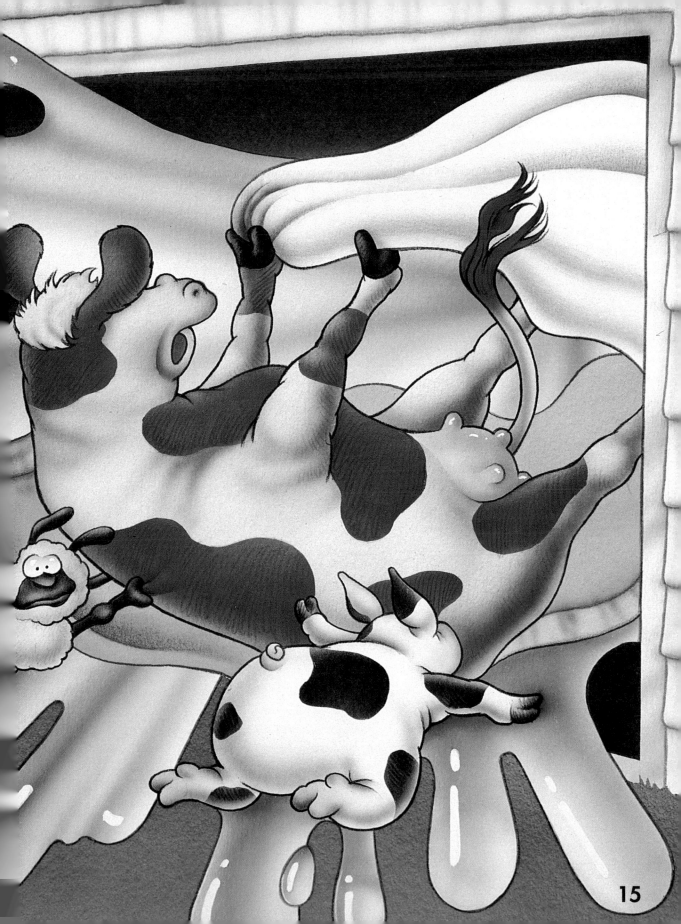

Back in the barn,
the animals said,
"Hay is the best
for a warm dry bed."